SEP 96

KN

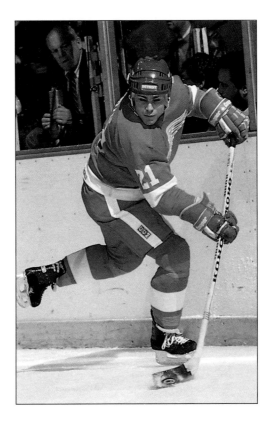

CREATIVE EDUCATION

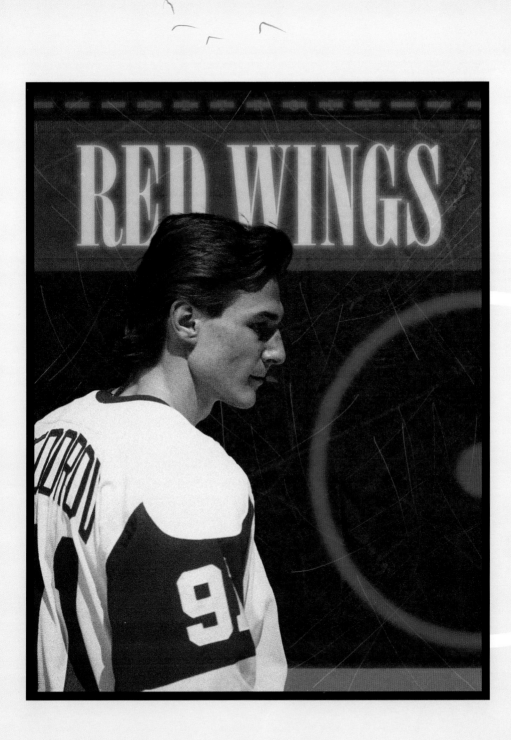

RED WINGS

VARTAN KUPELIAN

Published by Creative Education
123 South Broad Street, Mankato, Minnesota 56001
Creative Education is an imprint of The Creative Company

Designed by Rita Marshall
Cover Illustration by Rob Day

Photos by: Bettmann Archives, Bruce Bennett Studios, Focus on Sports,
Hockey Hall of Fame, Sports Photo Masters and Wide World Photos

Library of Congress Cataloging-in-Publication Data

Kupelian, Vartan.
Detroit Red Wings / Vartan Kupelian.
p. cm. -- (NHL Today)
ISBN 0-88682-674-8

1. Detroit Red Wings (Hockey team)--History--Juvenile literature.
[1. Detroit Red Wings (Hockey team)--History. 2. Hockey--History.]
I. Title. II. Series.

GV848.D47K87   1995   93-47951
796.962'64'0977434--dc20

123456

THE SHOWDOWN

In the spring of 1955, Alex Delvecchio was a 23-year-old center for the Detroit Red Wings and an emerging star in the National Hockey League. Usually a sound sleeper, Delvecchio tossed and turned in bed the night before the Wings' seventh-game Stanley Cup showdown against Montreal.

"I lay awake thinking of the game coming up," Delvecchio said. "It's the first time it ever happened to me."

It must have been a good omen. Delvecchio—not a bit tired—scored two goals and the great Gordie Howe added another as

Alex Delvecchio played for Detroit for 24 seasons.

Herbie Lewis led the newly-named Red Wings in goals (20) and assists (14).

the Red Wings defeated Montreal 3-1, capturing the Stanley Cup for the fourth time in seven years.

Delvecchio's goals were breathtaking. On the first, he cut across the goal mouth to send a 15-foot backhand shot past Montreal's famous goaltender, Jacques Plante, as more than 15,000 fans cheered. Delvecchio's second goal was a solo effort that came early in the third period to give Detroit an insurmountable three-goal margin against its archrivals, the Canadiens.

"It's a great thrill," said the unflappable Delvecchio, whose fine performance under pressure elevated him to star status. "It's always nice to beat Montreal and it's best in the Stanley Cup playoffs."

The Detroit Red Wings and the Montreal Canadiens were the outstanding teams of that era. Any series matching the two teams automatically had a place reserved in hockey history. But this Detroit team, according to the man who knew better than any other, was special.

"This is the greatest clutch team I've ever had," said Jack Adams, the Detroit coach. "They won every game that had to be won."

It was quite a tribute. For 40 years, the Red Wings were the model of a highly efficient and successful sports franchise. Their glory years produced seven Stanley Cup championships—more than any other United States–based NHL team. Many of the greatest names and personalities in hockey history have worn Detroit's distinctive winged-wheel crest, including Marty Barry, Larry Aurie and Ebbie Goodfellow from the early years (1926–48); Sid Abel, Terry Sawchuk and Gordie Howe in the glory years (1949–55); and Marcel Dionne, John Ogrodnick and Steve Yzerman from the modern era.

John Ogrodnick was a prolific scorer in the 1980s (page 7).

Coach Jack Adams, John Sorrell and Ralph Bowman contributed to the Wings' first Stanley Cup.

Founded in 1701 by French colonist Antoine de la Mothe Cadillac as a military and fur-trading post, Detroit is the automobile manufacturing capital of the world. The city's thriving industrial climate made it an attractive choice when the NHL entertained expansion possibilities in the spring of 1926. The awarding of a franchise to Detroit was of particular interest to Lester Patrick, who owned Western Hockey League (WHL) franchises in Victoria and Portland. As the NHL expanded, it hastened the collapse of the WHL. Patrick saw an opportunity to sell his teams to the new NHL franchise owners. He sold the Victoria Cougars to the new Detroit owners, who originally called their team the Detroit Cougars. The team's nickname was later changed to Falcons and, finally, to Red Wings when the club was purchased by industrialist James "Pop" Norris in 1932.

The first critical building block toward the ultimate goal of a championship was put in place with the hiring of John James "Jack" Adams as coach. Adams arrived in Detroit for the 1927–28 season and promptly went to work on building a winning foundation that would remain intact throughout his 35 years with the hockey club. Adams, who hailed from western Canada, was a star forward for teams in Toronto and Ottawa before coming to Detroit. There was never any question who ran the show with Adams around. He could be crusty or jolly but he was always in control.

Nobody knew the game better than Adams, and that knowledge was essential in moving the club up through the standings. By the mid-1930s, the Red Wings were the league powerhouse, winning Stanley Cup titles in both 1936 and 1937.

The 1936 playoffs produced one of the sport's most memorable moments. The opening game between the Red Wings and the Montreal Maroons was scoreless through three periods and five overtime periods. With 3:30 left in the sixth overtime period, Mud Bruneteau finally scored against Montreal goalie Lorne Chabot. The arena clock read 2:25 a.m. Detroit goaltender Normie Smith didn't allow a goal in the longest game ever played—176 minutes, 30 seconds. The Wings went on to quickly dispatch the Maroons, winning the series 3-0.

The Red Wings dominated the league again in 1937. Four Detroit players—right wing Larry Aurie, center Marty Barry, defenseman Ebbie Goodfellow and goalie Smith—were named to the six-man All-Star team. They had enough firepower to defeat the New York Rangers three games to two in the five-game final series for the Stanley Cup.

Adams' team won a third Stanley Cup in 1943, sweeping the mighty Boston Bruins in four straight victories, but the Red Wings at that time were just revving up for some truly great years ahead.

1 9 4 7

Tommy Ivan became coach and led Detroit to six first place finishes and three Stanley Cups.

GORDIE HOWE: A MAN FOR ALL SEASONS

An integral part of the Red Wings' success was the legendary Gordie Howe. His unique style of play, physical prowess and longevity in the sport enabled the star forward to set records few athletes will ever challenge.

No record is more notable than the length of his career. Howe made his NHL debut in 1946 and played in the NHL long enough to skate with his sons, Marty and Mark. His incredible career spanned five decades for a total of 32 professional seasons.

Adam Oates ranks among the team's playoff scoring leaders (pages 10-11).

Howe's physical presence earned him the nickname "Power" and added to his mythical status among players and fans. He stood 6 feet tall and weighed 200 pounds, with shoulders that sloped from a thick neck. He also had a mean streak that made him a fearsome opponent. If he felt an opponent had trespassed too far into his personal territory or taken advantage of a teammate, Howe doled out retribution discreetly and swiftly. Opposing players soon learned to avoid Howe and his domain.

Howe grew up in Floral, Saskatchewan, a small town in western Canada. He was an unassuming, fun-loving man who excelled at every sport he ever tried. He often joined baseball's Detroit Tigers at batting practice, where he frequently slammed balls deep into the stands. Football coaches looked at Howe and envisioned the perfect tight end. Howe was also an accomplished golfer with

a single-digit handicap. But hockey was the sport that was in his blood.

Howe's career was not without obstacles. He had to overcome several injuries, the most serious of which came in 1950 when he slammed into the boards while attempting to check Toronto's Ted Kennedy in a playoff game. Howe suffered a life-threatening head injury that required surgery and jeopardized his playing career. He recovered, however, and in the 1950–51 season tallied 43 goals and 86 points—his best output up to that point and good enough to lead the league in scoring for the first time.

In 25 seasons with the Red Wings, Howe won the scoring title and the Hart Memorial Trophy as the league's most valuable player six times each. He made the All-Star team 21 times. Years later, as a 50-year-old grandfather, he led the World Hockey Association's Hartford Whalers in scoring with 96 points.

"I'm doing what comes natural," said the man who defied the aging process. "I fell in love with the game when I was five years old. My mother had bought a sack for $1 from a lady she gave milk money to during the Depression. She didn't know what was in it. When she opened it, a pair of skates fell out. My sister and I each grabbed one. We went outside, she got cold and never saw the skates again."

1 9 5 2

Ted Lindsay was named to the All-Star team for the fifth of nine times.

GLORY DAYS: 1949–1955

With talent as monumental as Gordie Howe, Jack Adams assembled a Detroit powerhouse in the late 1940s and early 1950s that became one of the great dynasties in sports history. Beginning with the 1948–49 season, the Red Wings captured a league-record seven straight NHL regular-season cham-

1 9 5 2

Gordie Howe won his first of six Hart Trophies as the league's most valuable player.

pionships and four Stanley Cup titles. The famed "Production Line" (a reference to Detroit's automotive industry) consisted of Howe, Sid Abel and Ted Lindsay. Abel and Lindsay were tremendous players in their own right, and together the three future members of the Hockey Hall of Fame formed a lethal offensive machine for Tommy Ivan, who had taken over as coach from Adams. "They could score goals in their sleep," Adams said.

Lindsay, Abel and Howe finished 1-2-3 respectively in the league scoring race in the 1949–50 season en route to the first of four Stanley Cup championships. Pete Babando scored the winning goal in overtime in the seventh game of the finals against the New York Rangers.

Adams, now devoting himself entirely to managing duties, did a most unusual thing after that season. He broke up a winning combination with a big trade that sent goaltender Harry Lumley to Chicago. But the wily manager had his reasons. He saw the potential for greatness in 20-year-old goaltender Terry Sawchuk and wanted to give him a chance to play in the big leagues.

The results were spectacular. Sawchuk led the league with 11 shutouts in his rookie year. The Red Wings ended the regular season in first place, only to be eliminated in the playoffs. But Adams' move would pay long-term dividends. Sawchuk's outstanding goaltending skills helped the Red Wings win the Stanley Cup in three of the next four seasons.

One of the Red Wings' greatest seasons ever came in 1951–52. Howe won his second consecutive scoring title with 49 goals and 87 points. Teammates Howe, Lindsay, Sawchuk and defenseman Red Kelly made the All-Star team. During the playoffs that year, the Red Wings didn't lose a single game. Sawchuk posted four shutouts and allowed only five goals in the eight playoff games, a truly remarkable feat.

Dino Ciccarelli was among the NHL scoring leaders in 1992-93 (page 15).

1 9 5 5

Goaltender Terry Sawchuk won his third Vezina Trophy as the NHL's top goalie.

In 1954 Tommy Ivan added another Stanley Cup championship before turning the coaching position over to Jimmy Skinner. The Wings won the Cup again in 1955 when center Alex Delvecchio scored two key goals against Montreal in the deciding seventh game of the series.

It was during Detroit's glory years that one of the more unusual traditions in professional sports began. To mark the beginning of the playoffs, a local merchant and avid fan of the Red Wings threw an octopus onto the ice at Olympia Stadium. The eight arms of the octopus symbolized the eight victories needed to win the Stanley Cup. (In the NHL's original configuration of six teams, a team needed to win two best-of-seven series—a total of eight games—to capture the Stanley Cup.) Since then, at least one fan

Gordie Howe tops the NHL for most All-Star Team honors.

has tossed an octopus onto the ice for good luck at the opening game of every playoff series. Many NHL cities have adopted the practice along the way, but nowhere is it a more important tradition than in Detroit.

THE EXPANSION YEARS: THE 1960s

In the mid-1960s, the Red Wings still had Howe and a solid supporting cast, including centers Alex Delvecchio and Norm Ullman. But NHL expansion was just around the corner and about to change hockey's landscape. In 1967, the league added six new teams, doubling its size. Further expansion followed, with new teams being added every few years until the league reached 26 teams in 1993.

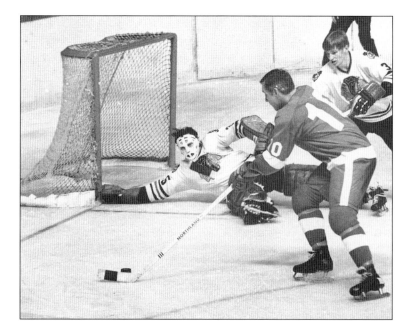

It became more difficult to win games, let alone dominate the league. There was also greater pressure to develop young players. The Red Wings, who had so many good older players, found it difficult to let go of the past.

In 1970, owner Bruce Norris (the son of original owner James Norris) made a bold and controversial attempt to resurrect the franchise. He hired a successful college coach, Cornell University's Ned Harkness, to introduce modern coaching and fitness techniques to the team. The results didn't match the good intentions and before long the Red Wings were a dissension-ridden club. The fallout included the departure of favorites Howe and general manager Sid Abel from the organization. Howe, by then a club vice president, severed his longtime association with the club to return to the ice with the Houston Aeros of the newly founded rival World Hockey Association. A curtain had dropped on another era of Detroit hockey.

1 9 6 8

Bill Gadsby, who had played five seasons with Detroit, took over the team's coaching duties.

LOOKING FOR ANSWERS: THE 1970s

The 1970s were a decade of transition as the team experienced many ups and downs but was unable to put together a string of successes. A right wing named Mickey Redmond became the Wings' first-ever 50-goal scorer, accomplishing the feat with 52 goals in 1973 and 51 in 1974. Left wing Danny Grant, who joined the team in 1974 in a trade with Minnesota, scored 50 goals in 1975. But the best player of the era was the dynamic Marcel Dionne, a diminutive French-Canadian who was the Wings' No. 1 draft pick in 1971. Setting team records for assists and points, Dionne quickly established himself as one of the league's finest players. However, after four seasons in Detroit during which the Red Wings finished no higher than fourth place in

Captain Marcel Dionne was unable to turn things around.

the Norris Division, Dionne was disillusioned with the club's progress. He signed as a free agent with the Los Angeles Kings. It would take the Red Wings 10 years before they would find another player to build the franchise around.

Coaches came and went with alarming regularity. The Wings failed to make the playoffs 15 times in 17 seasons. Former great players such as Ted Lindsay, Alex Delvecchio, Bill Gadsby and Marcel Pronovost were recruited for the front office to see if the glory from a previous era might rub off. It didn't.

Finally, owner Bruce Norris became so discouraged that he sold the Red Wings to Mike and Marian Ilitch on June 22, 1982.

Born in Detroit's West Side, Mike Ilitch made his fortune in the pizza business. He spared no expense on his new acquisition, spending money to sign free-agent players and top draftees. The overall result was impressive. Joe Louis Arena, which had opened in 1979 to replace the beloved Olympia Stadium, soon became an NHL hot spot, attracting huge crowds for every game. By the mid-1980s the Detroit franchise had emerged as one of the most financially successful in the NHL.

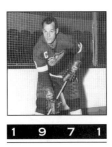

Gordie Howe ended his career in Detroit, leaving behind a host of NHL records.

THE COMEBACK: MAKING THE PLAYOFFS

The on-ice performance in the early years of the Ilitch era was promising. Jimmy Devellano was hired from the champion New York Islanders as general manager. His job was to rebuild the hockey operation, and to do that, he enlisted the help of Nick Polano as coach. Under the circumstances, Polano did a commendable job, getting the Wings into the playoffs in 1983 and 1984, ending a five-year drought.

Polano, who was also assistant general manager, played another role in improving the Red Wings. He was the club official who

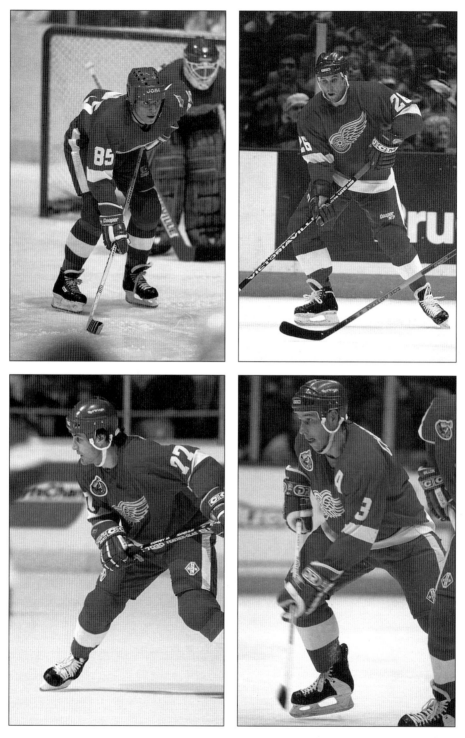

Left to right: Petr Klima, Ray Sheppard, Paul Coffey, Steve Chiasson.

spirited Petr Klima, a star player from Czechoslovakia, and Sergei Fedorov, a star from the former Soviet Union, out from behind the Iron Curtain and into Red Wing uniforms.

Already starring for the Wings when Klima and Fedorov arrived was Steve Yzerman, Detroit's No. 1 pick in the 1983 NHL draft. "Steve Yzerman will be the cornerstone of this team for many years to come," Devellano predicted on the day of the draft.

Despite assembling one of the most impressive ensembles in the league, the Wings' progress stalled. That's when Jacques Demers, an affable, emotional French-Canadian, was brought in to coach. He had put together an impressive coaching portfolio with the St. Louis Blues and in the rival World Hockey Association with Quebec and Cincinnati. In Detroit, the results were instant.

With Demers at the helm and Yzerman on the ice, the Red Wings began to turn things around. Demers' first act as coach was to name the 5-foot-11, 183-pound Yzerman team captain, and the smooth-skating center who grew up in Ottawa went on to eclipse all of Dionne's single-season team records.

In his first season, 1986–87, Demers coached the team from fifth to second place in the Norris Division and followed it up the next two seasons by capturing successive first-place finishes. The Wings reached the Campbell Conference finals two straight years, only to lose to Wayne Gretzky's Edmonton Oilers, the NHL's dominant team of the 1980s.

The disappointment weighed heavily on all concerned and resulted in many changes. Demers was fired and replaced by Bryan Murray, a longtime hockey man who had been coach of the Washington Capitals. While Yzerman continued to be one of the

1 9 8 7

Jacques Demers won his first of two consecutive Jack Adams Awards as Coach of the Year.

top stars of the NHL, racking up goals and points in club-record fashion, the Wings won a fair share of games but could not quite get over the line separating a very good team from a champion.

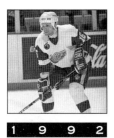

1 · 9 · 9 · 2

Rugged Vladimir Konstantinov was named to the NHL Upper Deck All Rookie Team.

THE MISSING LINK: A STANLEY CUP

Despite the Red Wings' greatest collection of talent since the glory days of Gordie Howe, the team continued to be stymied in the playoffs. They had not won a Stanley Cup championship since 1955.

In the summer of 1993, following another devastating play-off loss to Toronto, Ilitch moved once again to fill in the missing pieces. He hired Scotty Bowman, the all-time winningest coach in NHL history, to guide the Red Wings. Bowman had won five Stanley Cup championships while coaching Montreal in the 1970s and another with Pittsburgh in 1992.

Bowman's coaching prowess, combined with a talented array of skaters, heightened the team's hopes for a championship. But the results were not immediate. The Wings finished first in the West for the 1993–94 season but were beaten in the first round of the playoffs by the San Jose Sharks, a team making its first-ever Stanley Cup playoff performance.

The upset was one of the greatest ever in Cup play and sent shock waves throughout the organization. Bryan Murray was dismissed as general manager and Bowman was given additional responsibilities in the area of player personnel. One of Bowman's first moves was to acquire an established, proven NHL goaltender, Mike Vernon, from Calgary. Other changes took place throughout the summer of 1994 until Bowman and Ilitch were convinced the Wings were poised to end the championship drought.

Left wing Dallas Drake and right wing Dino Ciccarelli gave the game their all.   29

In 1992, Nicklas Lidstrom was runner-up for the Calder Trophy.

Mark Howe joined Detroit in 1992-93.

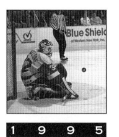

*The Red Wings'
emphasis during the
1995 season was
improved defense
and goaltending.*

The lineup now included two of the leagues's highest scorers, Yzerman and Sergei Fedorov, the NHL's Most Valuable Player for the 1993–94 season; veterans such as Dino Ciccarelli and Ray Sheppard; and youngsters Keith Primeau and former Soviet star Slava Kozlov. The defense was built around All-Star Paul Coffey, Bob Rouse, Mike Ramsey and two Europeans, Nicklas Lidstrom of Sweden and Vladimir Konstantinov from the former Soviet Red Army team.

"Now is the time to win the Stanley Cup," Ilitch had said the day he hired Bowman. "You've got to go with winners. Now, I like my chances."

So did a lot of other people as the Red Wings finished the lockout-shortened 1994–95 season with the league's best overall record and entered the Stanley Cup playoffs as a solid favorite. The Western Conference champions sailed through the first three rounds, combining an explosive offense with a stingy defense that stifled opponents at every turn.

The final between Detroit and New Jersey, a big, strong, physical team, shaped up as a classic. Nobody could have expected what was going to happen. The Devils got the jump on the unsteady Wings winning the first two games in Detroit. But as the Wings prepared for Game 3 in New Jersey, they remained confident of winning on the road and mounting an heroic comeback.

However, the Devils had their own agenda. They routed Detroit, 5-2, in the third game to the delight of their home fans and went on to complete a stunning sweep.

Once again, the Stanley Cup proved to be an impossible dream. But the 1994–95 season left an indelible mark on the Red Wings and their fans. They came so close to the treasured Stanley Cup they could see it and feel it. It was a glorious run that ended a mere four victories shy of the ultimate goal. The Red Wings are determined to build on their near-miss. The dream isn't over.